Look and Find®

Disney Princess

phoenix international publications, inc.

Thanks to her little friends, Cinderella has a dress for the ball! Can you find all of these helpers?
Gus
this bluebird
Jaq
this mouse
this mouse
this bluebird

Belle loves to read! The Beast's library is filled with books she is sure to enjoy. Look around and find these books for Belle:
Sunny Days Ahead
Petal Power
Friends of Philippe
Bird Words
Dragon Dramas
The Castle Chronicles
N
P
U
S
F
H
J
C
O
R
D
K

T
A
Y
M
H
G
V
Q
L
B
F
E
I
W
X

Painting, knitting, dancing, reading... Rapunzel has so many ways to pass the time in her tower! Look for these things she needs to be crafty:
palette
ballet slippers
beads
knitting needles and yarn
glue jar
guitar

Ariel collects things from the human world as she dreams about life on dry land. Can you find these treasures from her collection?
dinglehopper
pipe
birdcage
violin
compass
boot

Snow White can always find time to sing and dance with the Seven Dwarfs. When you find each of these instruments, make its musical sound!
concertina
flute
kazoo
triangle
lute
drum

Everyone in Agrabah is living happily ever after... including Jasmine and Aladdin! Can you spot these happy faces?
child
baker
Genie
Abu
merchant
Rajah

Merida doesn't want to get married. And unless one of her suitors can beat her at archery, she won't have to! Can you find all of these arrows?

Mulan is a hero! She went to war and helped save her country. Can you find the friends who wish her a safe journey home to her family?
Cri-Kee
Chien-Po
Ling
Mushu
the Emperor
Little Brother

Cinderella's friends used lots of supplies to trim her pretty dress. Can you find and count each item below?

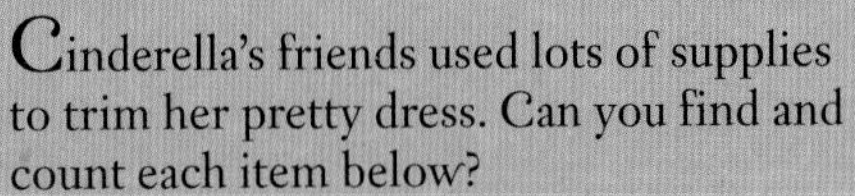

1 dress stand
2 baskets
3 pairs of scissors
4 red pincushions
5 pink ribbons
6 balls of yarn
7 spools of thread
8 pink bows
9 white buttons

Turn back to the Beast's library and look for all the letters of the alphabet.

As you find each one, say its name out loud.

Rapunzel stays busy with these big-and-little pairs. Return to the tower and see if you can find them all:

big sketchbook • little sketchbook
big feather pen • little feather pen
big paint jar • little paint jar
big ribbon • little ribbon
big vase • little vase
big doll • little doll

Ariel doesn't always know the real names of human things in her collection. She thinks a fork is a dinglehopper! Can you make up funny names for these treasures while you search for them under the sea?

toothbrush
necklace
clock
hat
book
plate